Pip the Penguin

by Janet Stutley
illustrated by Philip Webb

Table of Contents

Chapter I
Pip the Chick

Pip the emperor penguin started life as an egg. His mother, Peggy, laid the egg just before she went away. It was a beautiful white egg. She was very proud of it.

All the females left together. They were traveling across the ice to find food. They walked toward the sea under a stormy sky.

"Isn't this fun?" they giggled.

Pip's father, Philip, watched as the females left. He balanced Peggy's egg on his feet to keep it warm. His feathers fluttered as the wind blew across the Antarctic ice and snow.

All of the other fathers in the colony had an egg to look after, too. They knew it was an important job.

Pip hatched from the egg just before Peggy came back with fish. Pip was hungry and his mom fed him some fish. It quickly vanished down his throat.

"This is your mother, Pip," said Philip. "You know, we are emperor penguins."

"Ohhhh," sighed Pip with surprise. "Does that mean we will live in a great big castle? Will we travel around in a golden coach?"

"No, Pip," answered his mother. "We live out here on the snow and ice, just like all the other emperor penguins!"

Pip's father had eaten nothing during the two months Peggy had been away. Now he was going on his own fishing trip with the male penguins.

"Where's that basket, Peggy?" he said.

She handed him the basket. "Good-bye, dear," she said, giving him a peck on the cheek. "Catch plenty of fish!"

Pip snuggled under the belly fat above his mother's feet. He was warm there.

Chapter 2
Cool School!

Pip stayed on his mother's feet for another two months. Then his father returned. By that time, Pip had grown so much that Philip hardly recognized him!

"You are getting to be a big fellow," smiled his father.

"Will I ever be as big as you?" asked Pip, looking up at the large male penguin with the basket of fish.

"You will someday," said Peggy. She took her husband's basket. "Thank you, dear."

Pip and the other young penguins were now old enough to hang out alone. They met together without their parents for the first time and began squawking and chattering. They were very noisy.

"Hello," said a young female penguin. "I'm Penny!"

"I'm Pip," Pip replied.

One old penguin, Mrs. Fishywinter, had offered to look after the young penguins. She tried to teach them some fishing and swimming tips. But they were young and foolish. They fluttered and flapped around, and giggled a lot. They didn't think they needed to learn anything.

"Listen here!" cried Mrs. Fishywinter, but no one did.

Then she said they could play on the ice.

Pip and Penny threw snowballs at each other and slid on their tummies.

"This school is cool!" cried Pip.

Chapter 3
Cracking Up

Life was fun for Pip and the other penguins. Every day they played on the ice. They slid, wiggled, and waddled. They got to know the other young penguins very well.

Then the weather started getting a bit warmer. The ice began to break up. The cracks in the ice came nearer and nearer to where the penguins lived.

Every morning the adult penguins spoke to the younger ones.

"Be careful, Pip," warned his mother.

"Stay close to our colony and out of the water," warned his father.

But Pip just looked down and played with his scarf. He was wondering how many snowballs he could make in one day.

One day Penny and Pip began playing a new game. One of them would grab the other one's hat and throw it as far as he or she could.

Penny was winning. She'd had a lot of good throws!

Then Pip threw her hat. It sailed across the ice and landed near the edge of the water.

Pip jumped up and down with great joy. "Now I'm winning!"

Penny ran down to get her hat. She wanted to win the next throw.

All of a sudden, a crack cut across the ice next to Penny. She peered into the water. It looked dark and scary below the snow.

Pip flapped his wings. He squawked loudly at Penny. "LOOK OUT!"

Chapter 4
Sink or Swim?

Penny was worried. She fell straight through the crack in the ice, and down into the water. Splash!

Pip was scared. What could he do to save Penny?

Just then Penny popped up in the water. She could swim!

"Look at me!" Penny shouted happily, swimming around in circles.

"Here I come!" yelled Pip, jumping into the water with a big splash. He could swim, too!

Their parents stood nearby and smiled. They knew the time had come for Pip and Penny to begin their own fishing. The young penguins would be able to take care of themselves next winter.

And so they did.

Comprehension Check

Retell the Story

Use an Inference Chart and the pictures to help you retell this story.

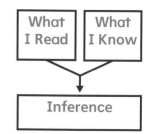

Think and Compare

1. Turn to page 3. Why do the father penguins stay behind while the mothers go to the sea? *(Make Inferences)*

2. How is Mrs. Fishywinter's school like your school? How is it different? *(Analyze)*

3. Why is it important that young animals learn how to look after themselves? *(Evaluate)*